We Like to Play

By Pamela Chanko

ISBN: 978-1-338-88855-3

Editor: Liza Charlesworth
Art Director: Tannaz Fassihi; Designer: Tanya Chernyak
Photo ©: 3: Bull&;#39;s-Eye Visual Arts/Shutterstock.com. All other photos © Getty Images.

1 2 3 4 5 6 7 8 9 10   68   31 30 29 28 27 26 25 24 23
Printed in Jiaxing, China. First printing, January 2023.

SCHOLASTIC INC.

I like to play soccer.
I have fun!

I like to play softball.
I have fun!

I like to play basketball.
I have fun!

I like to play tennis.
I have fun!

I like to play football.
I have fun!

I like to play hockey.
I have fun!

We like to play together.
We have fun!